WILFRID | SCOTTY | TOOTS | DANNY | SMIFFY | HARSHA | SIDNEY | FREDDY | MANDI | 'ERBERT | PLUG

THE BASH STREET KIDS

WE'RE GOING TO USE THE SCHOOL LIBRARY TO CARRY OUT SOME RESEARCH FOR YOUR HISTORY PROJECTS.

SCHOOL LIBRARY

HMPH! CAN'T WE JUST USE THE INTERNET LIKE EVERYONE ELSE?

THE LIBRARY IS THE *ORIGINAL* INTERNET! ALL INFORMATION IS HERE, WITH NO ADDED DISTRACTIONS!

SCHOOL LIBRARY

QUIET PLEASE

DON'T WORRY, PLUG! THE LIBRARY HAS GOT COMPUTERS!

BET I CAN BEAT YOU AT 'CAR BOXING 3'!

GAH! NO COMPUTERS!

HERE ARE THE HISTORY BOOKS! START RESEARCHING!

HISTORY

GROAN!

TOSS

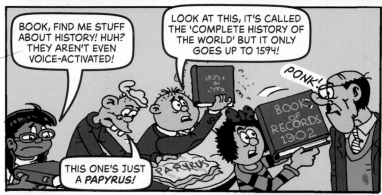

BOOK, FIND ME STUFF ABOUT HISTORY! HUH? THEY AREN'T EVEN VOICE-ACTIVATED!

LOOK AT THIS, IT'S CALLED THE 'COMPLETE HISTORY OF THE WORLD' BUT IT ONLY GOES UP TO 1594!

PONK!

BOOK OF RECORDS 1902

THIS ONE'S JUST A *PAPYRUS!*

PAPYRUS

THEY'RE SO OLD THEY'RE FALLING APART!

IT WASN'T ME! I DIDN'T DO ANYTHING!

I THINK IT'S A SEPARATE BIT OF PAPER! WHAT DOES IT SAY?

OPEN!

DROP!

THUD!

COR! IT LOOKS LIKE A *TREASURE MAP!*

I SMELL AN *ADVENTURE!*

WAFT!

NO, I THINK THAT WAS JUST ME!

Ye Beano Town

16TH CENTURY TREASURE MAP!

WHEN LITTLE ERIC EATS A BANANA, HE BECOMES...

BANANAMAN

IT'S *'THE KING-SIZED KERFUFFLE'* ON THE WRESTLING CHANNEL TONIGHT! I'M SO EXCITED!

BUT THAT WILL HAVE TO WAIT! MY CRIME ALERT BANANA IS GOING OFF!

BRIIING!

TIME TO EAT A BANANA AND TURN INTO...

FAZOOM!

B

...BANANAMAN!

GENERAL BLIGHT AND DOCTOR GLOOM! WHAT ARE YOU UP TO THIS TIME?

WHO? US?

WE'RE JUST HAVING A NICE DAY OUT!

WHAT ARE YOU GOING TO TRY TO DO TO ME THIS TIME? TURN ME INTO CUSTARD? SET FIRE TO MY TOES? REPLACE MY UNDERWEAR WITH SQUIRRELS?

NOPE! WE'RE NOT GOING TO TRY TO DO ANYTHING TO *YOU*.

WE'RE GOING TO DO SOMETHING TO *OURSELVES*!

ZAP!

WE'RE MAKING OURSELVES STRONGER! BIGGER! *TOUGHER*!

RIIIIP!

RAAR! AND ALSO *GRR*!

GULP!

NOW WE'RE BIGGER THAN YOU, THERE'S ONE THING THAT WE WANT TO DO...

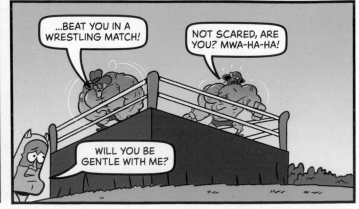

...BEAT YOU IN A WRESTLING MATCH!

NOT SCARED, ARE YOU? MWA-HA-HA!

WILL YOU BE GENTLE WITH ME?

MINNIE THE MINX
SHE'S TOUGHER THAN ALL THE BOYS...

DANGEROUS DAN
BEANOTOWN'S TOP SPY!

LATER...

I DIDN'T THINK THIS THROUGH. SHE'S GOING TO FOLLOW ME AROUND ALL DAY WAITING FOR ME TO TAKE THIS OFF.

HUFF! PUFF!

TICK-TOCK, HEENA!

KEEP OUT! THAT MEANS YOU, HAARSHA!

WE'RE GOING TO GO FROM WARRIOR POSE TO MANGLED MONGOOSE...

...AND I'M NOT EVEN ASKING ABOUT THE BUCKET!

HNNNGH!

SNIGGER!

SWEAT!

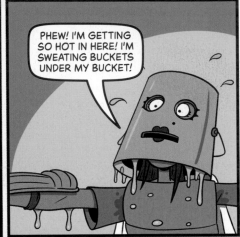

PHEW! I'M GETTING SO HOT IN HERE! I'M SWEATING BUCKETS UNDER MY BUCKET!

ARRGH! FINE! I'M GOING TO HAVE TO TAKE THIS THING OFF!

WOW! THAT'S BETTER!

OKAY, HARSHA... DO YOUR WORST!

GASP! THE SMELL FROM INSIDE THAT SUIT... ACK! I CAN'T STAND IT! GROO!

IT SMELLS LIKE SOMEONE WAS SICK ON SOME OLD CHEESE!

SHE'LL NEVER PRANK ME AGAIN, ALL I HAVE TO DO IS STOP WASHING!

HMM... THAT IDEA STINKS, HEENA! - ED

HAR HAR'S JOKE SHOP!
MEET BEANOTOWN'S FUNNIEST FAMILY!

I'M GOING TO GET HEENA WITH THESE WATER BALLOONS!

SHE'S GOING TO GET SUCH A...

CLUNK!
CLANK!
CLANG!

...HUH? WHAT'S THAT NOISE?

SPLAT!

HA! YOUR PRANKS CAN'T PENETRATE MY *PRANK-PROOF SUIT OF ARMOUR*, HARSHA!

BAH!

THUNK!
THUNK!

YOUR RUBBER ARROWS ARE COMPLETELY INEFFECTIVE!

DEFLECT!

AND YOUR ITCHING POWDER MERELY FALLS OFF ME!

GAH!

STINK BOMBS HAVE NO EFFECT ON ME EITHER!

ACK!

WHOOSH!

HA-HA! I AM *INDESTRUCTIBLE*!

THIS WAS A GREAT IDEA OF MINE! WHILE I'M IN THIS SUIT, I'M COMPLETELY PRANK-PROOF!

YOU'LL HAVE TO TAKE THAT SUIT OFF EVENTUALLY, HEENA! AND WHEN YOU DO...

...I'LL BE WAITING!

ANGEL FACE INVESTIGATES
Detective for hire!

BIFFO THE BEAR
Sillier than the average bear!

CALAMITY JAMES
The unluckiest boy in the world!

JJ
Freewheeling, freestyle fun!

EXCUSE ME, I JUST NEED TO GET A DRINK.

FEELING THE HEAT, DAN? HEH-HEH!

LEMONADE, PLEASE. NOT SHAKEN OR STIRRED, OR IT'LL FIZZ EVERYWHERE.

WHAT'S THE LATEST, Q?

THE PREFECT IS CHEATING. TAKE A CLOSER LOOK.

HE'S USING X-RAY SPECS TO SEE THE CARDS, THEN GETS THE CARD HE NEEDS SENT TO HIM.

I KNEW HE HAD TO BE CHEATING!

CARD-O-MATIC

IF HE WANTS TO PLAY DIRTY, THEN WE'LL PLAY DIRTY! I'M NOT LOSING THE WORLD IN A GAME OF SNAP!

SO...

I'M READY TO PLAY ON, MIND IF I DEAL?

IF YOU THINK IT'LL HELP! HA-HA!

YOU CAN GO FIRST!

I WAS GOING TO ANYWAY!

PREFECT

YEEOOOWCH!

HE'S GOT CARDS UP HIS SLEEVE!

WHAT?

LOOK, EVERYONE! THE PREFECT WAS CHEATING!

FLUTTER!

SNAP!

GET OUT OF HERE, YOU BIG CHEAT!

WAAH! HELP!

I DON'T THINK THAT WAS THE KIND OF SNAP THE PREFECT HAD IN MIND! CHUCKLE!

ZOOM!

THE ORDINARY GIRL WITH THE EXTRAORDINARY BEST FRIEND!

READ MORE ABOUT BETTY'S ADVENTURES LATER IN THE ANNUAL! - ED

RUBI'S SCREWTOP SCIENCE

DOO-DOO-DE-DOO!

RUBI, DO YOU WANT TO GO TO THE PARK? THE ICE CREAM VAN'S THERE!

UM... RUBI? PROFESSOR? ANYONE?

ROOAR!

ARRGH! DON'T EAT ME, I PROBABLY TASTE HORRIBLE!

SORRY, PIE FACE! I'LL JUST TURN THEM OFF!

ME AND DAD HAVEN'T RECREATED A BUNCH OF DINOSAURS FROM FROZEN MOSQUITO DNA OR ANYTHING, IF THAT'S WHAT YOU'RE THINKING!

IT SEEMED PRETTY *REAL* TO ME! HOW DID YOU DO IT?

I'LL SHOW YOU, IT'S ACTUALLY PRETTY SIMPLE!

IT'S ALL GOOD, OLD-FASHIONED SMOKE AND MIRRORS REALLY! EACH OF THESE DRONES HAS A DIGITAL PROJECTOR ATTACHED TO IT...

...WHEN THEY ALL COME ON, THEY'RE ABLE TO CREATE A PERFECT THREE-DIMENSIONAL ILLUSION! BECAUSE THE DRONES CAN MOVE AROUND, THE IMAGE CAN TOO!

THAT'S REALLY CLEVER!

ANGEL FACE INVESTIGATES — Detective for hire!

ANGEL FACE AND JENNY ARE AT THE SCENE OF ANOTHER HORRIBLE CRIME...

SO YOU'RE SAYING THERE WERE THREE CHOCOLATE OATY BISCUITS IN THIS TIN, BUT NOW THERE ARE NONE?!

NO! ONLY ONE WENT MISSING. THERE SHOULD BE TWO LEFT!

MUNCH!

MUNCH!

I BLAME MYSELF FOR CALLING YOU GUYS!

WE FORGIVE YOU.

BIFFO THE BEAR — Sillier than the average bear!

I'M TAKING UP BOXING TO KEEP FIT!

NOW I'LL REALLY LIVE UP TO MY NAME!

BIFF! BIFF! BIFF!

LEW STRINGER

BIFF!

OW!

YEP, FROM NOW ON, WE'LL CALL YOU BIFF-OW THE BEAR!

GROAN!

CALAMITY JAMES — The unluckiest boy in the world!

MY SOCKBOY COSTUME'S BOUND TO WIN.

FIZZY MILK

COMIC CON TODAY! GRAND PRIZE FOR WINNING COSTUME

IS JAMES THE REAL SOCK-BOY?

INSIDE...

OH NO! EVERYONE'S DRESSED UP AS SOCKBOY! LUCKILY, I THOUGHT THAT MIGHT HAPPEN.

SO...

GROO! THE PONG!

TEE-HEE!

BUT...

OH NO! I ALSO SCARED AWAY THE JUDGES! COME BACK!

URK!

GAG! WHIFF! PONG!

JJ — Freewheeling, freestyle fun!

COME ON, EVERYONE! LET'S HUSTLE!

KRRRR!

OH, COME ON, REF! THAT WAS CLEARLY A FOUL!

BEANOTOWN CHESS CHAMPIONSHIP

TAKE HIM DOWN! WHOO! YEAH!

DENNIS AND THE GOLDEN WHOOPEE CUSHION! PART ONE!

DENNIS HAS FOUND ANOTHER COOL THING AT HAR HAR'S JOKE SHOP...

SWEET!

WHERE DOES YOUR DAD GET ALL THESE AWESOME THINGS, HARSHA?

BILLY BEANO'S PRANK FACTORY.

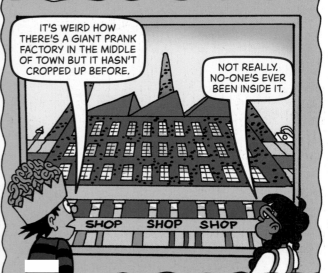

IT'S WEIRD HOW THERE'S A GIANT PRANK FACTORY IN THE MIDDLE OF TOWN BUT IT HASN'T CROPPED UP BEFORE.

NOT REALLY, NO-ONE'S EVER BEEN INSIDE IT.

SHOP SHOP SHOP

MAHIRA · **KHAD** · **STEVIE** · **CUTHBERT** · **WILFRID** · **SCOTTY** · **TOOTS** · **DANNY** · **SMIFFY** · **HARSHA** · **SIDNEY**

THE BASH STREET KIDS

DANNY'S SENT ME A PICTURE OF THE NEW CLUE HE FOUND! IT SAYS, 'TO FIND THIS CLUE FREE OF SCORN, FIND THE PLACE WHERE BOOKS ARE BORN!'

WHAT COULD THAT MEAN?

WELL, OBVIOUSLY IT'S, ER...

...GAH! THINKING IS TOO HARD!

I WISH WE'D GOT CUTHBERT ON OUR TEAM!

MAYBE WE SHOULD ASK A WRITER! THEY KNOW ALL ABOUT BOOKS!

BUT WHERE DO WE FIND ONE?

HEY, I'M A WRITER! HOW CAN I HELP?

TOSS!

THAT'S A STROKE OF LUCK!

RUBBISH SKIP

OKAY, MR WRITER, WHERE ARE BOOKS BORN?

WHAT AN INTERESTING QUESTION!

REJECTED

I GUESS YOU COULD SAY THAT BOOKS ARE BORN IN THE WRITER'S BRAIN, THAT'S WHERE THE INITIAL SPARK OF AN IDEA BEGINS!

AH!

TAP! TAP!

TAP! TAP!

TAP!

OOH!

THE CLUE MUST BE IN HIS BRAIN!

GET IT OUT!

GET OFF ME!

YOU PESTS! GET OUT OF HERE!

THUD!

THUD!

OLD SCRIPT

ARE ALL WRITERS THIS CRANKY?

THAT IDEA WAS A WRITE-OFF!

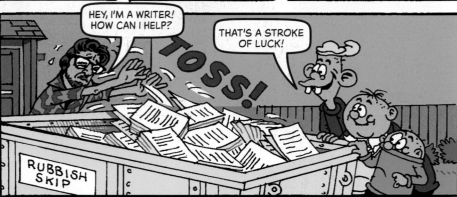

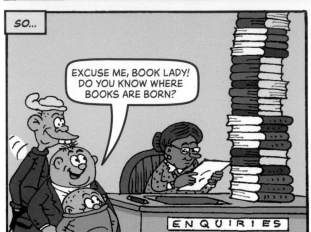

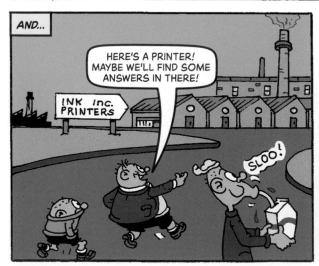

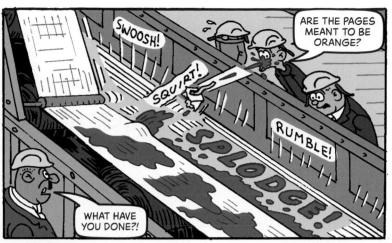

MINNIE THE MINX

SHE'S TOUGHER THAN ALL THE BOYS...

I WONDER HOW MINNIE GOT ON WITH HER FIRST DAY AT BADGER SCOUTS AND IF SHE GOT A BADGE?

Beanotown Badger Scouts

AS LONG AS SHE HASN'T *BADGERED* ANYONE!

MMMPH! MMMPH! MMMPH!

THAT'S GOT TO BE WORTH A *FIRST AID BADGE!* CHORTLE!

I HATE IT WHEN I'M RIGHT.

SO SORRY ABOUT THAT. MINNIE CAN BE A BIT... ENTHUSIASTIC.

YEAH! I SHOULD GET AN ENTHUSIASM BADGE!

YOU'RE NOT GETTING ANYTHING! YOU'RE *BANNED!*

OH YEAH? MAYBE I'LL MAKE MY *OWN* SCOUTS WITH MY *OWN* SCOUT HUT AND MY *OWN* BADGES AND MY *OWN* FURIOUS MAN!

COME ON, MIN, HOME.

I CAN'T BELIEVE YOU'VE BEEN BANNED FROM ANOTHER SCOUT GROUP! YOU'VE ALREADY BEEN KICKED OUT OF THE VOLES, THE TERRAPINS, THE BUDGERIGARS AND THE OCELOTS!

THERE'S NO SCOUTS LEFT THAT'LL TAKE YOU!

WE'LL SEE ABOUT THAT!

SO...

ALL RIGHT, TROOPS, WELCOME TO MIN'S MEGALODONS, THE BEST SCOUT GROUP IN BEANOTOWN AND NOT ALL MEAN AND UPTIGHT LIKE THE OTHER ONES!

MIN'S MEGALODONS SCOUT GROUP

WAHOO!

I WAS PROMISED FOOD! WHERE'S THE FOOD?

WHEN LITTLE ERIC EATS A BANANA, HE BECOMES...

BANANAMAN

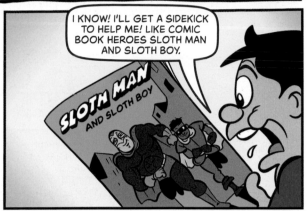

GENERAL BLIGHT HAS BROKEN OUT OF JAIL. I SHOULD TURN INTO BANANAMAN AND STOP HIM!

BUT I'M LATE FOR SCHOOL! WHAT SHOULD I DO?

I KNOW! I'LL GET A SIDEKICK TO HELP ME! LIKE COMIC BOOK HEROES SLOTH MAN AND SLOTH BOY.

SLOTH MAN AND SLOTH BOY

WHEEE! BEING A SUPERVILLAIN IS FUN!

I'LL HOLD AUDITIONS AT SCHOOL FOR SIDEKICKS! THIS WILL BE FUN!

IF I'M GOING TO FIND A SIDEKICK, I NEED TO EAT A BANANA AND TURN INTO...

FAZOOM!

...BANANAMAN!

BUT HOW AM I GOING TO CHOOSE A SIDEKICK? THERE ARE SO MANY KIDS! I DON'T WANT ANYONE TO FEEL LEFT OUT!

I NEED HELP!

WHEEEE!

UMM... GENERAL BLIGHT?

COULD YOU HELP ME FIND A SIDEKICK? YOU'LL BE FIGHTING THEM EVERY WEEK, SO YOU SHOULD GET A SAY IN WHO I CHOOSE!

HEH-HEH-HEH! OF COURSE!

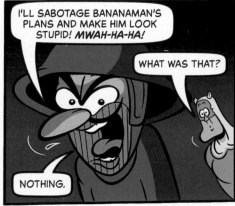

I'LL SABOTAGE BANANAMAN'S PLANS AND MAKE HIM LOOK STUPID! MWAH-HA-HA!

WHAT WAS THAT?

NOTHING.

SO...

I FEEL LIKE IT'S MISSING SOMETHING.

SUPERHERO SIDEKICK TRY-OUTS AT 3PM

DANGEROUS DAN
BEANOTOWN'S TOP SPY!

I GOT YOUR MESSAGE, Q! A BIT UNUSUAL TO SEND IT BY BUZZARD, THOUGH! OW!

PECK!

WE CAN NEVER BE TOO CAREFUL, DAN! WE DON'T WANT ANYTHING FALLING INTO ENEMY HANDS! PLUS WE RAN OUT OF PIGEONS.

ANYWAY, WE RECEIVED THIS BROADCAST FROM S.M.I.R.K.* EARLIER TODAY!

PECK!

*SECRET MINISTRY OF INTELLIGENT ROTTERS KOMMITTEE. - ED

PEOPLE OF EARTH! THIS IS THE PREFECT, CONTACTING YOU FROM MY MOON BASE.

ON THE MOON!

S.M.I.R.K.

I HAVE A GIANT LASER POINTED AT EARTH, AND UNLESS I GET A TRILLION GABILLION POUNDS, I WILL BLOW IT UP!

EARTH, I MEAN.

PREFECT

THAT'S SO ANNOYING!

ANNOYING? THAT'S PUTTING IT MILDLY! IT'S EVIL! DESPICABLE! THE BIGGEST THREAT WE'VE...

...YOU WERE TALKING TO THE BIRD, WEREN'T YOU?

PECK!

SORRY! HE'S BEING A PEST!

MUNCH!

HE ISN'T EVEN WEARING A SPACESUIT.

GASP! HE'S FAKED THE MOON LANDING!

SOMETHING SEEMS OFF ABOUT ALL THIS... HOW CAN THE PREFECT AFFORD A TRIP TO THE MOON?

I THOUGHT ONLY TECH BILLIONAIRES COULD DO THAT?

ALSO, LOOK... THE LIGHTING IS OFF AND THE FLAG SHOULDN'T BE ACTING LIKE THAT IN SUCH LOW GRAVITY.

THE ORDINARY GIRL WITH THE EXTRAORDINARY BEST FRIEND!

BETTY IS ON HOLIDAY AT YETI'S HOME...

URRGH! THIS IS SO GROSS!

BETTY LOOK LIKE LITTLE YETI NOW!

I HOPE SO. IT'S MY FIRST DAY OF YETI SCHOOL AND I WANT IT TO GO WELL.

I'M SURE YETI SCHOOL IS A DOODLE WHEN YOU'RE AS SMART AS I AM!

AT YETI SCHOOL...

I'VE GOT A FEELING THIS IS GOING TO BE, ER... VERY EDUCATIONAL!

THIS YETI COUSIN, GRUNTY!

IT'S A PLEASURE TO MEET YOU AND ATTEND YOUR FINE EDUCATIONAL ESTABLISHMENT, MISS.

HUH?

SIGH. FINE... GRUNT!

MAYBE AN APPLE WILL WIN HER OVER!

GRUNTY BROUGHT APPLE.

BLECH!

THIS FOR YOU!

TASTY!

IT SEEMS YETI'S A STAR STUDENT, BUT I'LL SOON IMPRESS EVERYONE ONCE CLASS STARTS!

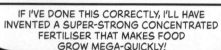

AND...

THEY JUST KEEP REPLICATING! IF THEY DON'T STOP, THEY COULD ENGULF BEANOTOWN! DAD ISN'T BACK UNTIL LATER AND I CAN'T EVEN GET TO MY EQUIPMENT!

WHY DO WE HAVE THESE KINDS OF PROBLEMS? I HAVE NO IDEA WHAT TO DO!

FEAR NOT! I CAN HELP!

ARE YOU GOING TO EAT THE TURNIPS TO STOP THEM FROM REPLICATING?!

EW! TURNIPS ARE GROSS! I SAY WE LET THOSE GOATS LOOSE ON THEM, THEY'LL EAT ANYTHING!

IT'S WORTH A SHOT!

IT'S ACTUALLY WORKING! PHEW! GOOD IDEA, PIE FACE!

I RELATE TO GOATS, WE BOTH HAVE BOTTOMLESS TUMMIES!

MUNCH!

CHOMP!

IT'S A GOOD JOB YOU *TURNIPED* WHEN YOU DID!

DISASTER AVERTED! ALTHOUGH I WOULD HAVE LIKED TO GET MY HANDS ON THE CONTROL TURNIP FOR FURTHER INVESTIGATION!

BURP!

COME ON, WE'VE GOT SOME ICE CREAM IN THE LAB!

RESULT!

BURBLE!

POP!

UH-OH! YOU'VE GOAT TO BE KID-DING ME! - ED

ANGEL FACE INVESTIGATES — Detective for hire!

BIFFO THE BEAR — Sillier than the average bear!

CALAMITY JAMES — The unluckiest boy in the world!

JJ — Freewheeling, freestyle fun!

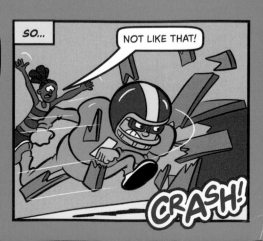

DENNIS & GNASHER UNLEASHED

DENNIS IS PLAYING IN BEANOTOWN WOODS...

TAKE THAT, TREE! AND THAT! AND THIS!

YOUR REIGN OF TERROR IS AT AN END!

SWISH!

I WONDER WHAT THE TREE DID.

COME ON, GNASHER. LET'S SEE WHAT ELSE WE CAN FIND.

OW!

GNA-HA! TREE REVENGE!

DEEPER IN THE WOODS, DENNIS FINDS THE RUINS OF A SMALL CASTLE...

WOW!

THREE BRICKS!

THIS RUINED CASTLE IS THE MOST RUINED CASTLE IN THE COUNTRY! - ED

HALF BURIED BEHIND THE RUINS, DENNIS FINDS...

A HELMET!

PUT ME DOWN!

ARRGH!!

I'VE CHANGED MY MIND! PICK ME UP!

ARE YOU A GHOST?

NO, I'M A HEDGEHOG! OF COURSE I'M A GHOST!

CAN YOU HELP ME FIND MY ARMOUR AND MY ETERNAL RESTING PLACE?

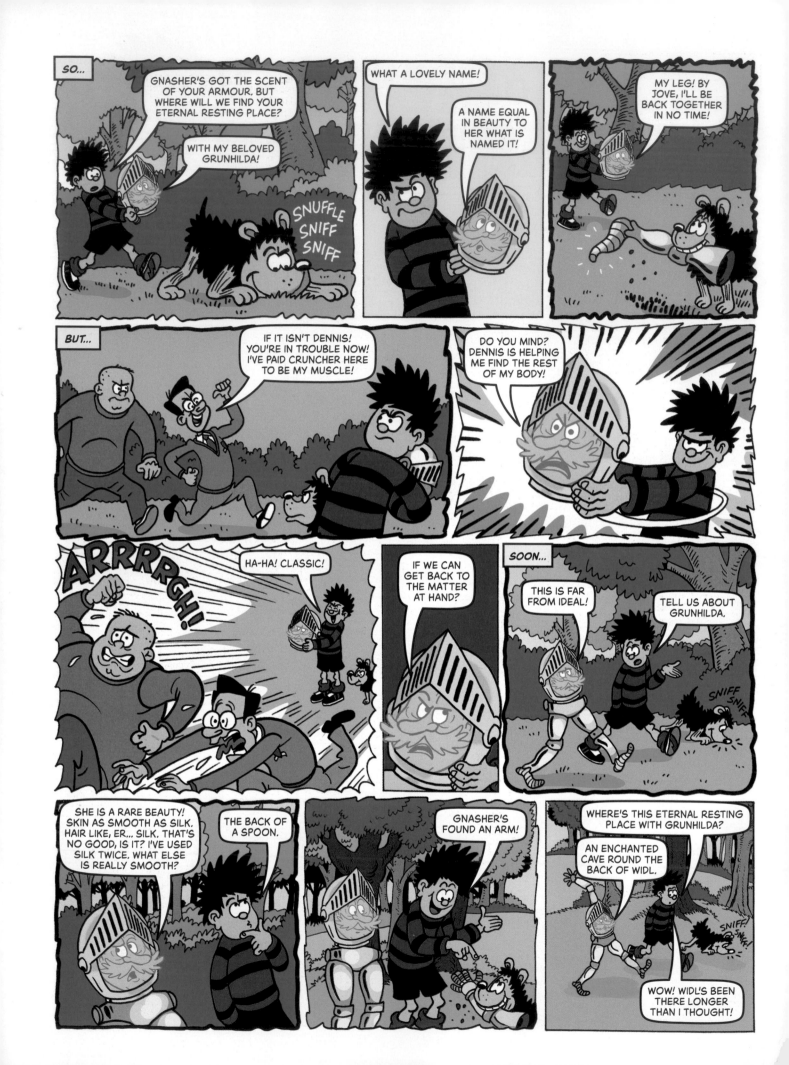

ANGEL FACE INVESTIGATES Detective for hire!

A WAVE OF OATY CHOCOLATE BISCUIT THEFTS HAS HIT BEANOTOWN, BUT ANGEL FACE AND JENNY ARE ON THE CASE...

THIS IS A MAP OF ALL THE OATY CHOCOLATE BISCUIT THEFTS.

GOOD WORK, JENNY. CAN YOU TAKE AWAY THE ONES THAT WERE US?

YUP. THERE YOU GO.

A PATTERN! WHAT'S THAT LIGHT BROWN DOT IN THE MIDDLE?

THAT'S JUST A BIT OF BISCUIT, I'LL HAVE THAT!

BIFFO THE BEAR Sillier than the average bear!

I'VE TRAINED AND NOW I'M READY FOR MY MISSION!

THE COUNTDOWN BEGINS! 5... 4... 3... 2... 1...

...ZERO! THIS IS IT! BIFFO IN SPACE!

I THINK YOU'RE TAKING THIS RIDE FAR TOO SERIOUSLY, BIFFO!

WHEEEE!

BEANOTOWN FAIR ALL THIS WEEK

CALAMITY JAMES The unluckiest boy in the world!

I'D LIKE A NEW HAIRSTYLE THAT MAKES ME LOOK LIKE A MOVIE STAR!

MIRROR MIRROR ON THE STAND WHO IS THE UNLUCK- IEST IN THE LAND?

SNIP! SNIP!

THERE YOU ARE! WHAT DO YOU THINK?

ARRGH! WHICH MOVIE STAR AM I MEANT TO BE?

GLEAM!

MIRROR MIRROR IN MY HAND WHO IS

PROFESSOR X FROM 'X-MEN' OF COURSE!

PROFESSOR X

JJ Freewheeling, freestyle fun!

OUT!

WOW! YOU'RE AMAZING AT CATCHING, JJ!

WHAT CAN I SAY? I JUST HAVE AN INBUILT *CATCHING* ABILITY!

GASP! IS THAT THE TIME? GOTTA GO!

GAH! I MISSED IT!

NOT SO GOOD AT *CATCHING* THE BUS, THOUGH!

ROGER THE DODGER
IN AROUND THE WORLD IN 70 DODGES!

YIKES! THAT PIE I MADE REALLY DID A NUMBER ON THE DISH! IT'S WELDED ON!

DARLING! COULD YOU WASH THE PIE DISH?

I'D LOVE TO, MY SWEET!

TUM-TI-TUM!

WHAT?! THAT'LL TAKE AGES TO GET OFF!

THERE MUST BE A WAY TO DODGE THIS.

LIKE FATHER, LIKE SON. - ED

ROGER!

IN THE LIVING ROOM...

UH-OH! MY DODGER SENSE IS TINGLING!

THREAT OF HAVING...

...TO DO SOMETHING!

ROGER! COME AND WASH THIS PIE DISH!

YIKES! TIME TO SCRAM!

ZOOM!

OUT FRONT...

HMM... I WANT TO CHILL IN THE HAMMOCK IN THE BACK GARDEN, BUT I CAN'T GET PAST DAD IN THE KITCHEN...

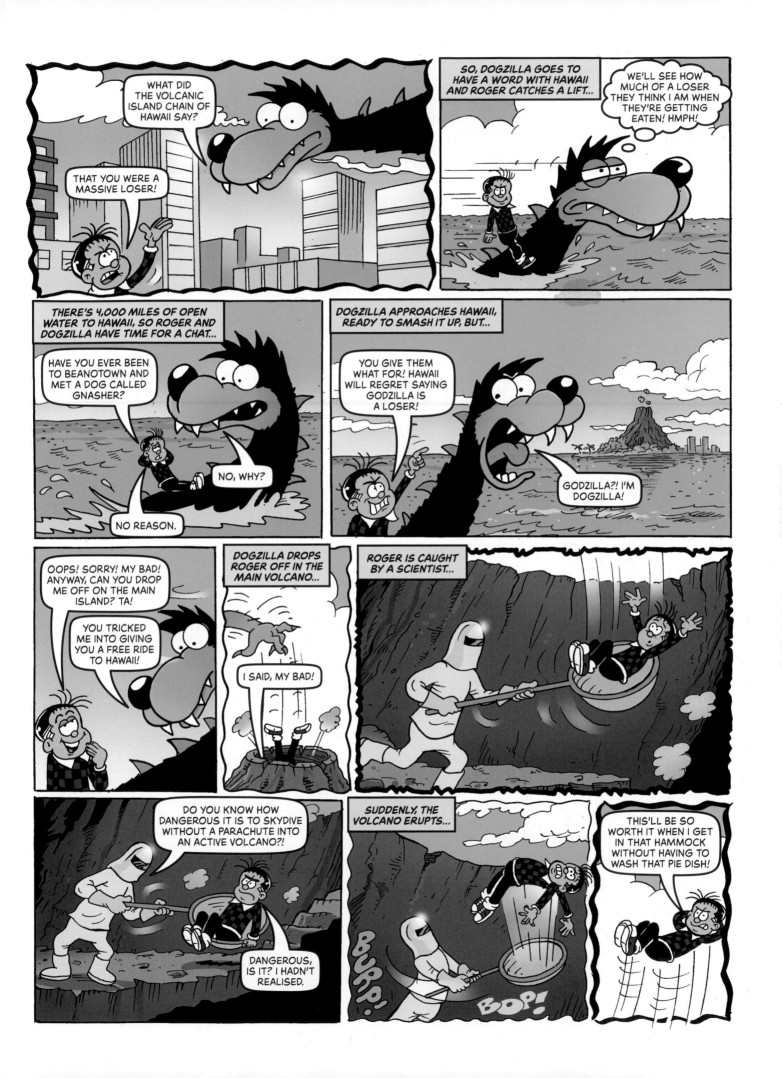

ROGER STARTS TO FALL AGAIN BUT, AS LUCK WOULD HAVE IT, A PLANE WAS PASSING...

INSIDE THE PLANE...

ER, STEWARDESS... SOMEONE'S KNOCKING ON THE DOOR!

KNOCK KNOCK!

THAT MIGHT BE MY FAULT. I JUST ORDERED A NECK PILLOW ON PRIME.

THEY LET ROGER IN...

FINALLY! IT WAS FREEZING OUT THERE!

MIND IF I SIT HERE? WHAT MOVIES HAVE WE GOT AND WHERE'S THIS PLANE ACTUALLY GOING?

SAN FRANCISCO.

CAN I HAVE A LEMONADE, PLEASE? BUT PUT IT IN A CHAMPAGNE GLASS.

IN SAN FRANCISCO...

EXCUSE ME, IS NEW YORK NEAR HERE?

IT'S ABOUT 3,000 MILES AWAY.

BUT...

120 DOLLARS?! I DON'T HAVE THAT MUCH!

I HAVE ZERO DOLLARS!

BUS STATION

GREY DOG

HMM... HOW TO GET ACROSS AMERICA WITHOUT TRYING... AND FOR FREE?!

SO...

WELL, THEY'RE GOING THAT WAY ANYWAY!

UNFORTUNATELY, HALFWAY TO NEW YORK, IN KANSAS...

UH-OH! A TWISTER!

SHOO!

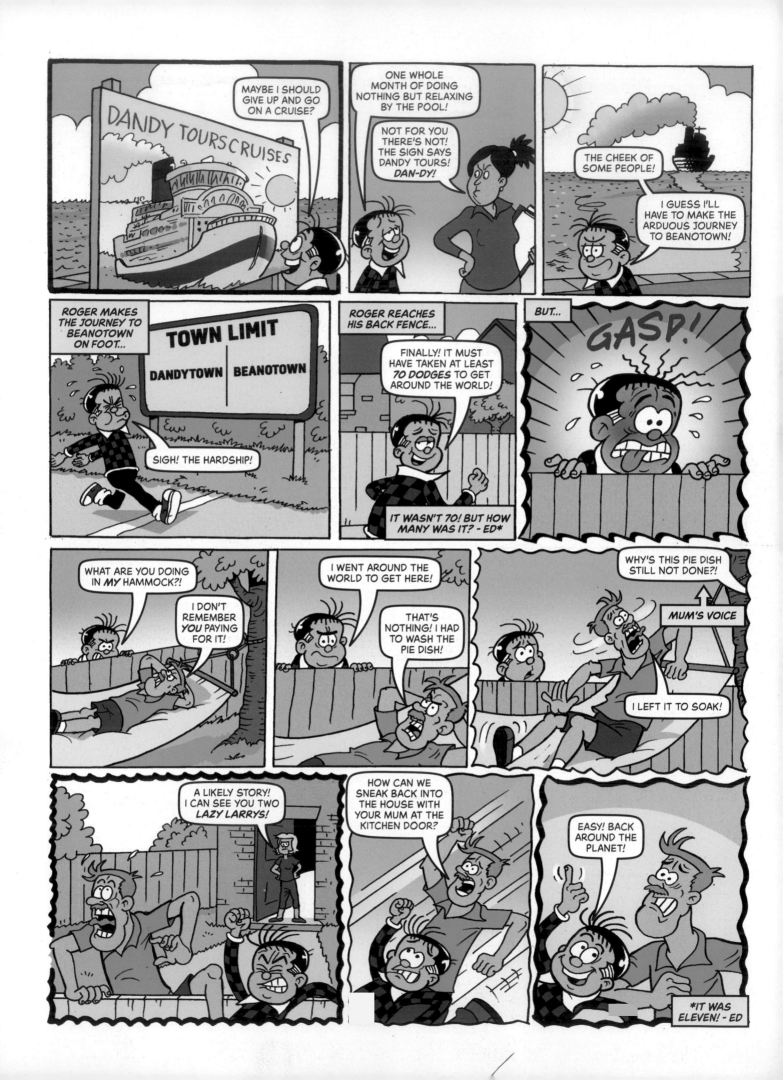

ANGEL FACE INVESTIGATES — Detective for hire!

BIFFO THE BEAR — Sillier than the average bear!

CALAMITY JAMES — The unluckiest boy in the world!

JJ — Freewheeling, freestyle fun!

DENNIS & GNASHER UNLEASHED

AS SEEN ON CBBC!

DENNIS AND PIE FACE ARE FIGHTING ALIENS DURING WORLD WAR TWO...

THIS GAME'S VERY *EDUCATIONAL*. THEY DON'T TELL YOU ABOUT THE ALIENS IN HISTORY LESSONS!

PEW! PEW! PEW!

JJ ARRIVES...

ARE YOU TWO STILL ON THAT GAME?

WE'RE ONLY AT THE BIT OF WORLD WAR TWO WHERE THE ALIENS USE ZOMBIE DINOSAURS AGAINST US!

DON'T LEARN HISTORY FROM VIDEO GAMES, READERS! – ED

DON'T SIT AROUND ON YOUR GAME ALL DAY! GET FIT! GET MOTIVATED!

DID MY MUM *PAY* YOU TO SAY THAT?

YES, BUT THAT'S NO REASON NOT TO! COME ON! TO THE TRACK!

AT THE RUNNING TRACK NEAR BEANOTOWN WOODS...

I'M A BIT TIRED, JJ, I NEED AN ENERGY...

ENERGY DRINKS ARE BAD FOR YOU! ALL THAT SUGAR AND CAFFEINE IS...

I'M NOT TALKING ABOUT A DRINK, I'M TALKING ABOUT AN ENERGY *PIE!*

COULD I HAVE AN ENERGY PIE TOO?

HORROR!

GIMME THAT! THERE'S NO SUCH THING AS AN ENERGY PIE!

HERE, GNASHER.

IT MUST BE MY BIRTHDAY!

GNASH! GNASH!

TOSS!

GNASH!

PING!

ENERGY!

FITNESS!

ALERTNESS!

GNASHER RACES AROUND THE TRACK IN SECONDS...

HMPH!

THAT WAS A VEGETARIAN PIE FROM VEGESTAN!

WHOOOSH!

THE BASH STREET KIDS

FIND OUT WHERE THE LAST CLUE LEADS LATER IN THE ANNUAL! - ED

MINNIE THE MINX

SHE'S TOUGHER THAN ALL THE BOYS...

MIN! COME QUICK! YOU GOTTA SEE THIS! A TRUCK CARRYING COLA ACCIDENTALLY TIPPED OVER ONTO A TRUCK CARRYING MINTS!

NOW THIS I *HAVE* TO SEE!

HOLD IT RIGHT THERE, MINNIE!

HUH?

I THINK YOU'VE GOT SOME CLEARING UP TO DO!

THAT COULD'VE BEEN *ANYONE* CATAPULTING MELONS INTO THE STREET!

MINNIE! DON'T FORGET WE'RE GOING OUT FOR DINNER IN A MINUTE!

GAH! I DID FORGET!

AW, I REALLY WANTED TO HANG WITH YOU, FRANCIS!

SOMETIMES I WISH I COULD BE IN LOADS OF PLACES AT ONCE.

WAIT A MINUTE... THAT GIVES ME AN IDEA!

SO, AT RUBI'S HOUSE...

NOW HOLD STILL, MINNIE, AND TRY TO CLEAR YOUR MIND. THIS CLONING MACHINE IS VERY SENSITIVE.

WE SHOULD BE ABLE TO GET A COUPLE OF EXACT COPIES OF YOU IN A FEW SECONDS!

DO THEY HAVE TO BE EXACT? I MEAN, I'M PRETTY UNIQUE!

STOP MESSING WITH THE SCIENCE. *CLEAR YOUR MIND!*

FZZT!

I MEAN, IF YOU COULD MAKE THEM JUST A LITTLE BIT DIFFERENT, THAT'D BE GREAT!

MINNIE! *STOP TALKING!*

DANGER

DAN

ANGEL FACE INVESTIGATES
Detective for hire!

ANGEL FACE AND JENNY ARE LOOKING INTO A SERIES OF OATY CHOCOLATE BISCUIT THEFTS...

I NEED TO TALK TO THE ORIGINAL THIEF WE CAUGHT AT THE START!

INSIDE BISCUIT JAIL...

WHAT'S GOING ON HERE?!

WHAT DOES IT LOOK LIKE? I'M BEING PUNISHED FOR MY CRIME!

CAKE, SIR?

I THINK I KNOW WHO THE MASTERMIND BEHIND THIS CRIME WAVE IS, AND WHY!

ME TOO! BUT I'M ONE OF THE BADDIES SO I'M KEEPING MY MOUTH SHUT!

APART FROM WHEN CAKE GOES IN!

FIND OUT WHO, LATER... - ED

BIFFO THE BEAR
Sillier than the average bear!

FAIR PLAY TO BIFFO, HE HAS A GO AT ANYTHING!

TODAY, HE'S CREATED HIS OWN FORM OF STREET DANCE!

GO, BIFFO!

BIFFO'S GOT SOME COOL MOVES! HE'S AN AWESOME DANCER!

DANCING? I'M TRYING TO SWAT AWAY THIS WASP! IT'S BEEN BUZZING AROUND ME FOR AGES!

CALAMITY JAMES
The unluckiest boy in the world!

I'M GOING TO GET MY FIRST A+ FOR THIS BRILL HOMEWORK I WROTE! IT TOOK ME HOURS!

HOME-WORK

I GOT A D-

BUT...

CRIKEY!

ZAP!

MARS

IN CLASS...

I'M AFRAID AN ALIEN ZAPPED MY HOMEWORK, SIR!

I GUESS THAT'S AN IMPROVEMENT ON SAYING THE DOG ATE IT!

SIZZLE!

HOMEWORK

JJ
Freewheeling, freestyle fun!

HEY, JJ! WHAT'S THE HARDEST THING ABOUT SKATEBOARDING?

IS IT THE DISCIPLINE AND HOURS OF PRACTICE? LEARNING ALL THE TRICKS? KEEPING YOUR BOARD IN GOOD CONDITION?

THE HARDEST THING ABOUT SKATEBOARDING IS DEFINITELY...

...THE GROUND! OOF!

WHAM!

DANGEROUS DAN
BEANOTOWN'S TOP SPY!

LOOK, IT'S DAN!

THERE HE IS!

HUH? DO THEY NEED ME TO SAVE THE DAY AGAIN?

YOU BURST MY BALLOON!

WHAT?

YOU TERRORISED MY CARROTS!

I DIDN'T!

YOU TRIED TO TAKE OVER THE TOWN!

I DEFINITELY DIDN'T DO THAT!

I AM DAN!

THEN EXPLAIN THIS!

I'LL PROVE IT ISN'T ME! COME ON!

SO...

THE PREFECT! I SHOULD HAVE KNOWN YOU'D BE BEHIND THIS!

MEET YOUR MATCH, DAN - YOU!

PEW!

I AM DAN! BEEP BOOP!

PEW!

THAT'S SUPPOSED TO BE ME?!

I AM DAN! BEEP BOOP!

I CAN'T BELIEVE ANYONE WOULD MISTAKE THAT FOR ME!

TWO DANS?! WHAT'S GOING ON? WHICH IS WHICH?

PREFECT

RUBI'S SCREWTOP SCIENCE

SH'UT!

UH-OH!

ZAP!

SORRY ABOUT THAT, PIE FACE. DAD WAS JUST...

...WAIT, WHERE ARE YOU?

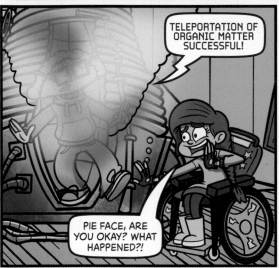

TELEPORTATION OF ORGANIC MATTER SUCCESSFUL!

PIE FACE, ARE YOU OKAY? WHAT HAPPENED?!

I DROPPED MY PASTY AND THE NEXT THING I KNEW I WAS OVER AT THE OTHER SIDE OF THE ROOM WITH A SAVOURY HEAD!

WAAH!

I HAVE NO IDEA HOW YOU DID IT, BUT YOU FIXED IT! THE TELEPORTER CAN NOW TRANSPORT LIVING MATTER!

UNFORTUNATELY, IT SEEMED TO THINK THAT YOU AND YOUR PASTY SHOULD BE *ONE THING* AND FUSED YOU BOTH AT A MOLECULAR LEVEL!

YOU CAN FIX IT, *RIGHT?!*

JUST GIVE ME A MINUTE!

MUCH LATER...

RUBI, PLEASE HURRY UP! I'M STARVING AND MY HEAD SMELLS *DELICIOUS!*

MAYBE IF I SEQUENCED IT THIS WAY...

BUT...

ARRGH! ALL THE DOGS IN BEANOTOWN THINK I SMELL DELICIOUS TOO!

I'M NEARLY THERE! JUST TRY TO STAY UP SOMEWHERE HIGH FOR FIVE MINUTES!

I'VE GOT IT NOW, PIE FACE!

SO...

PHEW! YOU NEARLY MADE A REAL *DOGS' DINNER* THERE, PIE FACE!

I NEARLY *BECAME* A DOGS' DINNER!

BETTY AND THE YETI!

THE ORDINARY GIRL WITH THE EXTRAORDINARY BEST FRIEND!

WELL, IT'S BEEN A LOVELY TRIP, BUT I THINK I'D BETTER BE GOING NOW!

YETIS LIKE MESS, I SHOULD HAVE KNOWN!

ARRGH! MONSTER!

GASP!

MUMMY! DISGUSTY MONSTER!

WELL, THAT'S JUST RUDE!

WAAH! IT SCARY!

BACK HOME...

YETI PLAY NON-TENDO!

MUM! DAD! I'M BACK FROM THE SCHOOL EXCHANGE A BIT EARLY!

I WONDER WHAT BITS OF LANGUAGE OR CUSTOMS SHE LEARNT FROM HER EXCHANGE FAMILY?

GRUNT! TINY, EVIL HORSE!

FRRRT!

GRUNTING... FARTING... IT'S WORSE THAN WE FEARED...

HR

...SHE'S TURNED INTO A TEENAGER EARLY!

MEANWHILE, BACK IN NEPAL, IT'S LIKE BETTY WAS NEVER THERE...

MONSTER MERCH

HEE-HEE! SCARY!

ACORNS ACCEPTED HERE

I SPIED THE MONSTER!

OR MAYBE NOT! - ED

HAR HAR'S JOKE SHOP!
MEET BEANOTOWN'S FUNNIEST FAMILY!

HARI · SAHANA · HEENA · HARSHA · HANI

WE'VE BARELY HAD A CUSTOMER ALL DAY! WHAT'S GOING ON?!

IT'S EVER SINCE THAT MASSIVE BRANCH OF JOKE WAREHOUSE OPENED UP.

JOKE WAREHOUSE? *WHERE?!*

ERM... RIGHT *ACROSS THE STREET!* I'M SURPRISED YOU DIDN'T NOTICE, DAD!

OH, YEAH.

THAT'S IT! LET'S GO AND SEE WHAT'S SO SPECIAL ABOUT IT. RALLY THE TROOPS!

MUM! HANI! HEENA! FAMILY TRIP!

INSIDE JOKE WAREHOUSE...

THERE'S SO MUCH CHOICE!

IT'S SO SHINY!

OOGLY · GOOGLY · SQUIRT FLOWERS

WOW! THE WHOLE OPERATION IS RUN BY ROBOTS.

WHEE!

GASP! HEENA! SHAME ON YOU FOR BROWSING!

BUT IT'S ALL SO CHEAP!

FINE, I'LL PUT IT BACK.

VIVIAN · DOLLY · CLEO

PSST! DO YOU DELIVER?

BLIP!

BACK IN HAR HAR'S JOKE SHOP...

I'VE DONE SOME CALCULATIONS AND THERE'S ONLY ONE WAY TO COMPETE, WE'LL HAVE TO LOWER OUR PRICES!

NOOOO!

WHEN LITTLE ERIC EATS A BANANA, HE BECOMES...

BANANAMAN

LUNCHTIME AT BASH STREET SCHOOL...

I WONDER WHAT DELICIOUS FRUIT IS ON OFFER TODAY!

HURRY UP AND PICK SOMETHING.

THIS FRUIT DOESN'T LOOK VERY FRESH.

IT'S JUST AS FRESH AS IT WAS LAST WEEK AND THE WEEK BEFORE THAT!

WE NEED BIGGER, BETTER, FRESHER FRUIT!

RUUMBLE!

OKAY, MAYBE NOT QUITE THAT BIG! AND IT'S HEADING RIGHT FOR THE SCHOOL!

I GUESS THIS OLD BANANA WILL HAVE TO DO!

TIME TO EAT THIS BANANA AND TURN INTO...

FAZOOM!

...BANANAGRANDAD?!

WHAT'S GOING ON? WHY IS THERE A GIANT PEAR?

IT'S AN APPLE, YOU BUFFOON! LIKE ME, APPLEMAN! YOU DON'T HAVE AN ENEMY CALLED PEAR-MAN, DO YOU?

BECAUSE I WOULD BE VERY HURT AND UPSET IF YOU DID!

HERE, CATCH!

DOOF!

GRAAR!

HEY! THE SCHOOL IS THAT WAY! SMASH THAT UP!

CRASH!

THEY DIDN'T HAVE ANY BANANAS IN THE SHOP! ALL THEY HAD WAS THIS BANANA ICE LOLLY!

I GUESS THAT WILL HAVE TO DO!

I'LL USE IT TO BECOME... ICE BANANAMAN!

FAZ·OOM!

BRR! IT'S FREEZING!

SORRY TO GIVE YOU *THE COLD SHOULDER*, CHIEF, BUT I'VE GOT TO SAVE THE DAY!

ICE TO MEET YOU, WORMY!

GRR!

I'M AFRAID YOU'LL GET A *FROSTY RECEPTION* IN BEANOTOWN!

FWOOSH!

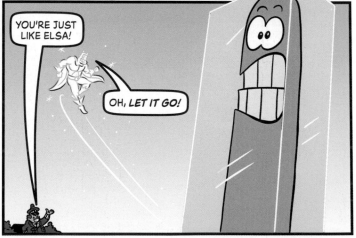

YOU'RE JUST LIKE ELSA!

OH, *LET IT GO!*

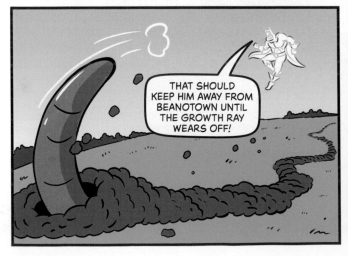

THAT SHOULD KEEP HIM AWAY FROM BEANOTOWN UNTIL THE GROWTH RAY WEARS OFF!

THE NEXT DAY AT SCHOOL...

RAAR!

WHAT HAPPENED TO ALL THE FRUIT?

DIDN'T YOU HEAR? FRUIT IS FAR TOO DANGEROUS FOR KIDS!

DENNIS AND THE GOLDEN WHOOPEE CUSHION! PART TWO!

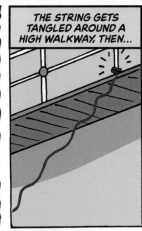

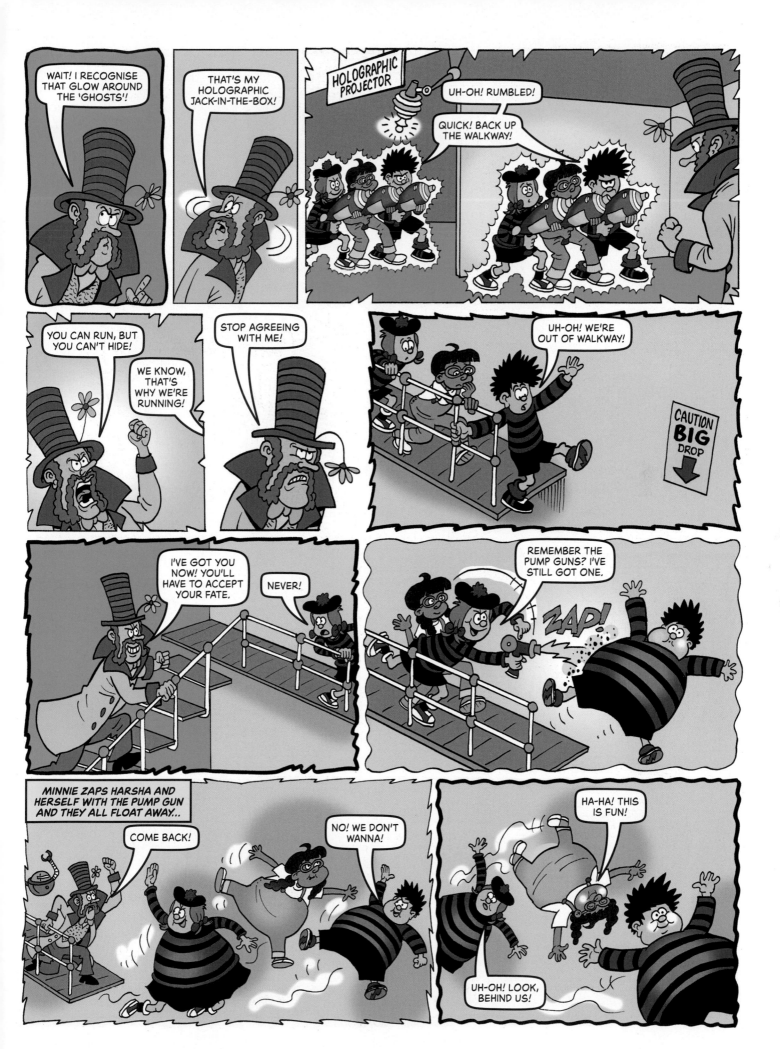

MINNIE THE MINX

SHE'S TOUGHER THAN ALL THE BOYS....

HI, FRANCIS! YOUR BATHROOM WINDOW WAS OPEN, SO I LET MYSELF IN.

WHATCHA DOING?

I'M READING ONE OF MY FAVOURITE MANGAS! THEY'RE JAPANESE COMICS!

THE ARTWORK IS PRETTY COOL, BUT THE STORY MAKES NO SENSE!

YOU'RE READING IT THE WRONG WAY!

IN JAPAN, THEY READ FROM RIGHT TO LEFT LIKE THIS, SEE?

OHHHH!

HAVE YOU GOT ANY MORE OF THESE?

YUP, LOADS!

MUCH READING LATER...

THAT WAS *EPIC!* BUT I NEED TO KNOW WHAT HAPPENS NEXT, LIKE *YESTERDAY!*

THE NEXT COMIC DOESN'T COME OUT FOR A WHILE YET!

IN THAT CASE I'LL HAVE TO MAKE MY *OWN* NEXT CHAPTER.

ZOOM!

HUH?

SO...

IT'S TIME FOR *ONE PINCH MIN* TO SAVE THE DAY!

WHOOSH!

WHOOSH!

RAAAARRRRGH!

TAK!

?!

HOW DID HE DO THAT? HE STOPPED MY FIST LIKE IT WAS... *NOTHING!*

WHAT POWERS DOES HE POSSESS?!

DRAMATIC, ISN'T SHE?

IT IS TIME I TAPPED INTO *THE MINX...* THE MOST POWERFUL FORCE ON EARTH.

YOU WHAT?

HYAAAAAAAAAARRRGGH!

WHOA! SHE'S GOING *MEGA-MINX!*

HUH?

FOOOSH!

IT'S TIME YOU SAW MY *REAL* POWER!

FIRE-FIRE-FIIIIIREBAAAAALL!

FAZOOM!

FAZOOM! KER-PSSSSSH!

IS SHE ALL RIGHT?

I HONESTLY DON'T KNOW.

I'VE HAD ENOUGH OF THIS. PREPARE FOR A *CRUNCHING!*

TOOOOOOOO...

...MAAAAATOOOOOO!

SPLUT!

WAAH!

THE WORLD IS SAVED BY *MANGA THE MINX!*

THAT WAS ANOTHER *FRUITFUL* DAY! CHUCKLE!

GRR! GET BACK HERE!

DENNIS & GNASHER UNLEASHED

AS SEEN ON CBBC!

ANGEL FACE INVESTIGATES
Detective for hire!

ANGEL FACE AND JENNY ARE ON THE CASE OF THE OATY CHOCOLATE BISCUIT THEFTS...

MAYOR BROWN! YOU'RE BEHIND THIS WAVE OF OATY CHOCOLATE BISCUIT THEFTS!

YES, I AM! THAT'S WHY MY BISCUIT JAIL IS SO NICE TO BISCUIT THIEVES!

SHUT UP! I WANTED TO SAY THAT!

I OWN THE BISCUIT FACTORY! I'M HAVING BISCUITS STOLEN SO PEOPLE HAVE TO BUY MORE BISCUITS!

STOP TALKING! I'M THE DETECTIVE, THIS IS MEANT TO BE MY BIT!

BIFFO THE BEAR
Sillier than the average bear!

BUSTER'S BEEN GROUNDED FOR PLAYING PRANKS SO I'M GOING TO HANG OUT WITH A DIFFERENT PAL TODAY!

I WONDER WHAT FUN ADVENTURES WE'LL GET UP TO?

YIKES! OF ALL MY BEANO PALS TO HANG OUT WITH, WHY DID I CHOOSE CALAMITY JAMES?!

CRASH!

BUZZZZ!

LEW STRINGER

CALAMITY JAMES
The unluckiest boy in the world!

WHAT A SWIZZ! MY NEW SHOES ARE SQUEAKING!

CURE FOR A SQUEAKY FOOT.

SQUEAK! SQUEAK! SQUEAK!

ARRGH! THAT CAT THINKS THERE'S A MOUSE!

LEAP!

SQUEAK!

WHIRL! SLASH! BITE! SCRATCH! TEAR!

NOW MY NEW SHOES ARE IN A WORSE CONDITION THAN MY OLD SHOES! JUST MY LUCK!

HOW TO GLUE A SHOE

JJ
Freewheeling, freestyle fun!

I'M ON AN EPIC QUEST THROUGH THIS DENSE UNDERGROWTH, SEARCHING FOR A LOST ARTEFACT.

THEY SAY IT CAN'T BE FOUND, BUT I KNOW IT'S HERE IN THE DEEP, DARK, MYSTERIOUS JUNGLE.

AHA!

I'VE FOUND IT, PIE FACE!

HAR HAR'S JOKE SHOP!
MEET BEANOTOWN'S FUNNIEST FAMILY!

HARI · SAHANA · HEENA · HARSHA · HANI

CALL US IF YOU NEED US. WE'RE JUST IN THE RESTAURANT DOWN THE STREET.

DON'T WORRY, MUM AND DAD! I'VE GOT EVERYTHING UNDER CONTROL.

AND I'LL MAKE SURE THESE LITTLE *MUNCHKINS* ARE ALL TUCKED UP IN BED ON TIME.

HEY!

YOU TWO HAVE FUN.

YOU'RE TURNING INTO SUCH A HELPFUL YOUNG LADY.

HAVE A GREAT TIME. GOODBYE! LOVE YOU!

DID YOU HEAR THAT, YOU TWO? *I'M THE BOSS* AROUND HERE NOW. HA-HA-HA!

UH-OH!

I'VE NEVER SEEN POWER GO TO SOMEONE'S HEAD THAT QUICKLY BEFORE.

GO UPSTAIRS AND GET WASHED AND READY FOR BED. AND NONE OF YOUR PRANKS!

SHORTLY...

HEENA! THERE'S A LEAK IN THE BATHTUB, THE SINK'S CLOGGED AND HANI THREW UP IN THE TOILET!

OH NO! I'D BETTER CALL DAD'S PLUMBER!

SO...

THANKS FOR COMING SO SOON. THE BATHROOM'S JUST HERE.

WC

MINUTES LATER...

CAN I HAVE A WORD?

SURE.

ANGEL FACE INVESTIGATES — Detective for hire!

WE DID IT, JENNY! WE SOLVED OUR BIGGEST CASE!

TAKE HIM AWAY, SERGEANT SLIPPER!

COME ON, MAYOR. IT'S BISCUIT JAIL FOR YOU!

OKAY.

YOU'RE SENDING HIM TO BISCUIT JAIL?! HE OWNS THAT JAIL AND IT'S LOVELY! EVERYONE GETS CAKE!

WE WANT TO GO TO BISCUIT JAIL! I PROMISE WE'VE PINCHED LOADS OF BISCUITS!

BIFFO THE BEAR — Sillier than the average bear!

IT'S CHRISTMAS EVE AND I'M SHORT-STAFFED! CAN YOU HELP ME, BIFFO?

YOU BET, SANTA!

AM I GOING TO BE HELPING MAKE ALL THE TOYS?

ERM... NOT QUITE!

STATION

RUDOLPH'S ON HOLIDAY AND YOU'RE THE CLOSEST THING TO A REINDEER!

SIGH. MERRY CHRISTMAS, READERS!

CALAMITY JAMES — The unluckiest boy in the world!

NOM! NOM! NOM! I LOVE EGGS! MUNCH!

JAMES! YOU'RE GONNA BE LATE FOR SCHOOL!

WE'LL EAT BREKKIE EN ROUTE!

OOPS! I DIDN'T EGGS-PECT THAT! WHIMPER!

TRIP!

SPECK OF DUST

SPLAT!

EGG WEEK IT WAS EGG-CELLENT

JJ — Freewheeling, freestyle fun!

I JUST TRIED TO GET SOMETHING FROM THE ATTIC BUT IT'S FULL OF BATS!

BLECH! BATS?!

MUM WAS RIGHT! THERE ARE BATS EVERYWHERE!

I REALLY SHOULD HAVE A CLEAR-OUT SOME TIME!

WANT MORE...
PUZZLES
COMICS
JOKES
PRANKS
PRIZES
...EVERY WEEK?
YULE LOVE IT!
WE MAKE IT REIN LAUGHS!
HAVE YOUR ELF A MENACING LITTLE CHRISTMAS WITH BEANO EVERY WEEK!
BE BORED SNOW MORE WITH...
BEANO.COM
BEANO
ON SALE EVERY WEDNESDAY!

RUBI AND PIE FACE SET TO WORK...

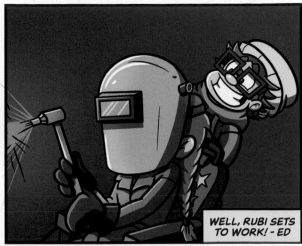

WELL, RUBI SETS TO WORK! - ED

WE'RE READY!

WOO! GO, TEAM PIE FACE!

THE MORNING OF THE RACE...

WE'RE THE FIRST ONES HERE! I CAN ALREADY TASTE VICTORY! OR MAYBE THAT'S JUST MY BREAKFAST! WHATEVER, IT TASTES *SWEET!*

JUST DON'T GET AHEAD OF YOURSELF, PIE FACE!

TWO HOURS LATER...

WHAT'S GOING ON? IT'S PAST THE START TIME!

PIE FACE, DO YOU HAVE THE POSTER AND RULES FOR THE RACE?

SURE!

ONE THING YOU NEGLECTED TO MENTION...

...IT'S A *NIGHT RACE!* OUR SOLAR-POWERED KART IS UTTERLY USELESS!

NOOOOO! I'LL NEVER KNOW THE SWEET TASTE OF VICTORY NOW!

LOOK ON THE *BRIGHT* SIDE, PIE FACE...

...YOU'VE A PRETTY *SWEET* RIDE TO GET YOU TO SCHOOL NOW!

WHEN LITTLE ERIC EATS A BANANA, HE BECOMES...
BANANAMAN

YAWN! ROBOT POODLES, GENERAL BLIGHT? IS THIS MEANT TO BE SCARY?

POUNCE!

I JUST WANTED SOME PETS, OKAY?

I'LL DEFEAT THESE PROGRAMMED POOCHES BEFORE YOU CAN SAY...

...ARRGH! THAT NIPS! GET THEM OFF ME!

CHOMP!

BITE!

HUH? I DIDN'T THINK THEY WERE THAT STRONG.

COME ON, ROBO-ROVERS, WALKIES.

GOOD DOGGIES! BLURBLE!

I FEEL LIKE I'M GETTING WEAK! I'M LOSING MY STRENGTH!

I'M GOING TO FLY TO PROFESSOR VON SCREWTOP'S LABORATORY. HE'LL BE ABLE TO TELL ME WHAT'S WRONG.

CRASH!

OUCH! I CAN'T EVEN FLY!

HOW WILL I GET THERE NOW?

SO...

ACACIA ROAD

BEANO

I'M LOSING MY POWERS, PROF! CAN YOU HELP ME?

DNA

I'VE BEEN STUDYING YOUR DNA. DNA IS IN EVERY ONE OF YOUR CELLS, IT'S A BLUEPRINT THAT TELLS YOUR BODY HOW TO GROW.

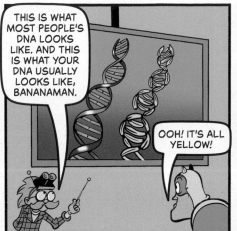

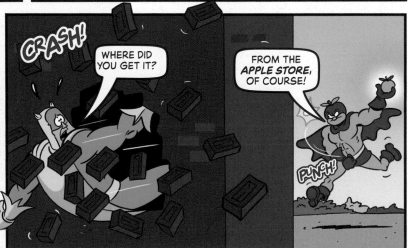

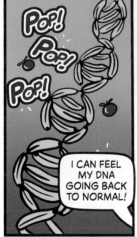

THE BASH STREET KIDS